Believe Practice Choose

The GIFT of SELF CARE

21 Tips for Your Self Care Tool Belt

Carole A. MacLean

Believe, Practice, Choose: The Gift of Self Care
21 Tips for Your Self Care Tool Belt

ISBN: 979-8-9852474-0-4
Library of Congress Control Number: 2021923936

Book Design by Michelle Radomski
Printed by IngramSpark

DISCLAIMER: THIS BOOK DOES NOT PROVIDE MEDICAL ADVICE

The information contained in this book is for informational purposes only. No material in this book is intended to be a substitute for professional medical advice, diagnosis, or treatment. Always seek the advice of your physician or other qualified health care provider with any questions you may have regarding a medical condition or treatment and before undertaking a new health care regimen, and never disregard professional medical advice or delay in seeking it because of something you have read in this book.

This book is dedicated to my daughter,
Margaret Harris MacLean,
a champion of self care who teaches me regularly
to be curious, creative, and caring.

Contents

· · · · · · · · ·

Introduction

· · · · · · · · ·

I've had many roles throughout my life: daughter, sister, wife, mother, banker, business owner, musician, writer, yogi, scrapbooker, photographer, hospice advocate. The list goes on. And through most of it, I was a "people pleaser," needing to make everyone happy and to ensure there was little conflict. I found out the body can only maintain a high level of activity and stress for a finite period before it lets you know when enough is enough.

After caring for my parents through the end of their lives, I realized I had been putting others before myself, and in doing so, neglecting both my physical health and my emotional wellness. Lack of sleep, poor eating habits, and worry, worry, worry had taken a toll. My body and mind were screaming at me to make a change. I was overweight, tired, and depressed. I could not show up in life the way I wanted to for my husband, my daughter, or myself. In fact, I was having a hard time finding a reason to get out of bed.

I knew I had to take action, and it had to start with self care.

I took my yoga practice more seriously and ate healthier whole foods. This led to a loss of weight, and I worked with my doctor to balance my hormones. I added meditation to my routine and then included visits with a therapist. I added extra appointments with my life coach, and eventually closed my business, which I had operated for 15 years. These changes cut my stress levels in half and gave me the energy to take care of myself.

I also started Fuzzy Red Socks Retreats, where I created for women a restorative space of sacred quietude away from the hustle and bustle of their busy lives. Each attendee receives a pair of socks to wear during the retreat and to take home with them. The socks are a symbol of self care—imagine sitting on the couch in your fuzzy red socks, curled up in a blanket, reading a good book, and sipping hot cocoa. In these retreats, through simple yoga poses, guided meditations, massage, and journaling, women begin their own journeys of self care with rest, reflection, and rejuvenation.

Throughout the book, I have chosen to spell self care with no hyphen. I am writing about **care of the self** where "self" is equally as important as "care."

I'm not a doctor or a nurse, nor do I have any certifications for teaching. I have created this book to help others who have found themselves, as I did, on a path leading toward destruction because of experiencing a traumatic event, being caregivers to others, or just realizing the effects of getting older.

I hope this book will be a resource for you. Read one tip a day for 21 days to start a healthy new habit. BELIEVE you matter, PRACTICE self care, and CHOOSE to love yourself. Then begin your journey toward improved health, abundant joy, and a life fulfilled.

*Self care is about
giving the world the best of you
instead of what is left of you.*

~ Katie Reed

What you believe,

you receive.

~ Gabby Bernstein

Believe

Believe

· · · · · · · · · ·

Day 1:
Believe Self Care
is Not Selfish

*Healthy selfishness . . . means we take care of our body and value our
needs, desires, feelings, and dreams. —Blake D. Bauer*

. . . .

Many of us have grown up believing we must put the needs of others first, before our own needs. Mother Teresa did this, right? I'm here to give you permission to let go of this erroneous belief. Put on your oxygen mask first.

Have you ever said, "I can't take a vacation or spend money on myself. I can't even make time to nap, take a walk, or relax. My spouse, my kids, my family, and my friends must come first?"

You're just a generous person, fulfilling your purpose, doing what's expected of you, right?

Wrong.

What you're doing is saying you don't matter, you aren't worth it, you come second, third, and fourth to everyone and everything in your life. This is why we must believe self care is not selfish and self care is crucial to being our best. We need to stop believing we don't matter and start replenishing our minds, bodies, and spirits. Only then can we be there for those we love and give of ourselves in a way that benefits everyone.

For years, I took care of my parents while they suffered from cancer and Alzheimer's. I watched them wither away in the latter part of their lives. I gave them all I had, and in the end, I had withered away, too. I was not being my best self for them—and I certainly wasn't being my best self for my husband and daughter. I became depressed, overweight, out of shape and so very sad because I gave away more than I had. I had nothing left for anyone I loved, including myself.

That's when I learned that self care is not selfish. That's when I started taking better care of myself. That's when I ramped up my yoga and meditation practices and lost weight. I closed my 15-year-old business. I got better at asking for help from my siblings, friends, and local organizations like the American Cancer Society. I did not know they had volunteers who could drive cancer patients to appointments. All this gave me the time to start my self care journey.

Start your self care journey by changing the way you look at selfishness and see how "healthy selfishness" can mean you have more to offer all those you love. Take time out for self care. With your renewed spirit and fresh new outlook on life, you and your loved ones will be grateful you did.

Quick Action Step:

Write on the following lines one thing
you can do today for self care.
Maybe it's as simple as closing your eyes for 5 minutes,
or scheduling a doctor appointment
you've been putting off,
or reading another tip from this book.

_____

_____

Believe

· · · · · · · · · ·

Day 2:
Believe in Yourself by
Investing in Yourself

The best investment you will ever make is in yourself. —*Warren Buffet*

· · · · · · · · · · ·

We all know how important it is to invest in our financial well-being by creating a budget, balancing our checkbooks, and adding to our savings and 401(k) accounts regularly. And investing in our physical, mental, and spiritual well-being—investing in ourselves—is just as important.

Self care for me is about investing in myself.

There are many ways to invest in you, such as learning a new skill, developing yourself personally or professionally, tapping into your creativity, or hiring a coach. Take the time to develop your gifts and talents.

When I started my self care journey, I knew the value of trusting my intuition and being creative, but I wasn't doing that anymore. It was time for me to get back to scrapbooking and pick up my camera. I set a goal of 15 minutes a day for hobby time.

My intuition told me to take command of my health. I returned to Weight Watchers, limited my sugar intake, and placed motivating quotes at my desk and on my bathroom mirror to remind me to be positive. I made appointments with my life coach so I would have someone in my corner cheering for me.

Each time I met a goal, my confidence increased. I felt happier, and my positive attitude returned. Each time I took baby steps toward one of these small changes, I felt stronger, and I moved closer to my old self.

Investing in myself is not something I do "only when I have time." It's non-negotiable for me. I make it a priority because I know what happens when I don't. I love the energy gained when I feel good about myself, and I love the unstoppable attitude I experience, knowing I am the best I can be. It didn't happen overnight, but now I know I'm not being selfish when I am doing things for myself. In fact, I believe taking care of myself is the greatest gift I can give to the people I love.

My 401(k) account may go up and down with the rise and fall of the often-unpredictable stock market. But when I invest in my physical, mental, and spiritual well-being, I increase my returns tenfold. Now there's a return on investment I can count on.

Quick Action Step:

Write on the following lines one way
you can invest in yourself today.
Could you return to a favorite hobby
or place positive affirmation notes
on your bathroom mirror?

_____

_____

Believe

. . . .

Day 3:
Believe Your Breath
is Your Friend

Your breathing is your greatest friend. Return to it in all your troubles and you will find comfort and guidance. —Teachings of Buddha Master

. . . .

The first time I saw my dad in a hospital bed after one of his many falls, I stopped breathing for a moment. When I heard my mother's diagnosis of throat cancer only a few short months after her diagnosis of early-stage Alzheimer's, I stopped breathing. The day I rushed to the emergency room to find my dad in a wheelchair, his arm in a sling, and my mother in bed being attended to by a doctor, I stopped breathing. I didn't have the tools then to help my body recover from the shock of those situations the way I do now.

Breath is a trusted friend you can call upon anytime, day or night. Using your breath as a self care tool doesn't take much time, is easy to do, and costs nothing. In five minutes or less, when you use your breath, you center yourself and help your body recover from the daily stresses of life. With each slow, deliberate, long breath, you are pouring unconditional love into your body, mind, and spirit.

Breathe in. Breathe out. Breathe deeply.

Breathing can provide many benefits to your physical and mental well-being. By changing our pattern of breathing, we significantly affect our body's experience of and response to stress. Through my yoga classes, I've learned that simple breathing exercises can reduce toxins, aid digestion, increase metabolism, develop mental clarity, and help achieve a state of deep relaxation and peace.

If only I had known this when I was caring for my parents.

Since then, I have discovered a new tool; a simple breathing exercise called square breathing or box breathing. You can practice it in the grocery store line, waiting in the doctor's office, or just before a big meeting at work. I often do it before an important phone call or a conversation I think might be confrontational or frustrating.

1. Begin by slowly exhaling all your air out of your lungs.

2. Gently inhale through your nose to a slow count of 4.

3. Hold at the top of the breath for a count of 4.

4. Gently exhale through your mouth for a count of 4.

5. At the bottom of the breath, pause and hold for the count of 4.

6. Repeat as often as you like.

Breath is the one self care tool you carry with you all the time. Use it often. Breathe in, breathe out, and breathe deeply. Lean on your trusted friend.

Quick Action Step:

Try this new breathing technique,
square breathing, at least once NOW
or write below when you will.

_____

_____

Believe

· · · · · · · · · ·

Day 4:
Believe Your Time
is Priceless

An inch of time is an inch of gold, but you can't buy an inch of time with an inch of gold.
—Chinese Proverb

. . . .

When I ran my business, there never seemed enough hours in a day to handle customer orders, train new consultants, or do paperwork. Often, I found myself conflicted with things to do for business, things to do for family, and things to do for myself. I was constantly looking for ways to squeeze out a few extra minutes. I couldn't just call up my company's warehouse and order more time.

Taking care of aging parents required me to be vigilant in this area. The day I returned from meeting with my mother's oncologist when we were told she required 10 weeks of 5-days-a-week radiation, I fell to the floor and sobbed. First, I ached for my mom and the agony this would cause her. Then I asked myself, "How will I get my mom to so many appointments every day, a 75-minute drive from my home?"

Believing my time was priceless was another important step in my self care journey.

I've read that people who manage their schedules well are happier, less stressed, and overall healthier in mind and body. We can't go to the store and buy additional time, but we can be more efficient in how we use what we have. And when we do, we're giving ourselves a gift.

I recovered from my deepest despair when I remembered how much I valued time. I reached out to others for help. I didn't have to do this alone. Before I knew it, I had a schedule filled with names of friends, family, American Cancer Society volunteers, and the days they would drive Mom to radiation treatments. The action I took saved me time and saved my sanity.

There are many ways to show you believe your time is priceless.

- Plan and prep meals for tomorrow.

- Ask someone for help.

- Stand up and do squats or march in place while working at your desk for some exercise.

- Plan your errands around town to limit how much you drive back and forth.

- Decide how long to spend on the computer checking email, shopping, or looking at Facebook. Then use a timer and stop when it goes off.

- Stock up on greeting cards so you don't have to run out at the last minute to get a card for someone.

- Use auto-refill on Amazon or Walmart for regular purchases, like kitty litter, paper towels, and prescriptions.

- Take 10-15 minutes every Sunday to plan your week and add these time saving tips to your schedule.

Now, before I agree to attend an event, volunteer, or get together with a friend, I look at my calendar and think about my priorities. Then I determine if it makes sense to say yes.

You deserve to have a less stressful life full of things you love to do. You deserve to feel happier, healthier, and whole. Start just one new timesaving idea and see how it goes. You might find getting more of this priceless commodity doesn't have to take a lot of time.

Quick Action Step:

Pick something from the list above you will do today to save time—or create another that is right for you and write it on the lines below.

_____

_____

Believe

· · · · · · · · · ·

Day 5:
Believe Your Body
Knows Best

If you listen to your body when it whispers, you won't have to hear it scream.
—*Project Happiness*

. . . .

I used to get sinus infections regularly. I struggled with low energy—and the fever, stuffy nose, and sore throat would keep me from sleeping well. I'd wake up feeling like a bus hit me. My to-do list would remain untouched, and the intense pressure in my head matched the pressure I put on myself to get better. As soon as I felt even the slightest bit improved, it would be a challenge to figure out if I should press forward, jump back into my schedule and go, go, go, or continue to take time to rest.

Now when things pile up and depression seems right around the corner, I remind myself of one of my basic self care rules: "Believe your body knows best and listen to it." I've learned to hear what my body has to say by slowing down and tuning in. I ask myself questions and I pay attention to the answers.

Just the exercise of talking to your body requires an awareness we seldom take time to practice.

"How are you today, lovely feet?"

"I appreciate you, strong back. Would you like a massage?"

"Thank you, long legs. What do you need today?"

It may seem awkward at first, but it becomes natural the more you do it. Ask your body what it needs and be willing to listen with patience and non-judgment.

As I paid attention to my body, I recognized the symptoms of a sinus infection before they were full blown. Instead of going on with my regular schedule, I slowed down, canceled my less important appointments, and went back to bed. I no longer ignored my body and wished away the inevitable. I took action and allowed my body to heal before it started to scream.

I pay attention in yoga class, too. If the yogi next to me is going deeply into a pose I know my body will not do, I go to my edge, a place of challenging my body without causing harm. I avoid comparing myself to others and pushing beyond what my body needs on any particular day.

And then, there are those "feelings." Our body communicates to us through feelings and emotions. I used to ignore how I felt. I hoped the anger, the fear, the embarrassment would go away. Now I give a name to what I'm feeling. "Today I am blue. I am embarrassed. I am afraid." By acknowledging what I feel, declaring it out loud, and taking the time to label my emotions, I can be proactive about how I want to deal with them. This process is much more productive than my former pattern of allowing my feelings to fester and boil up into something bigger.

What else does my body tell me? I need to get out of my chair and move. I need to stop watching the television and turn out the light. I need water, not a sugary drink, caffeine, or alcohol.

Believe your body knows best. Ask it what it needs. Listen to its whispers so you don't have to hear it scream.

Quick Action Step:

Write down the part of your body you are appreciating
the most at this moment and thank it out loud.
Is there some part of your body trying to get
your attention right now? What is it asking for?

_____

_____

Believe

· · · · · · · · · ·

Day 6:
Believe You Must
Nourish to Flourish

Food is fuel and not a solution to anything other than giving your body nutrients. I love chocolate like the next girl, but it's not going to change my situation. —Gabrielle Reece

. . . .

I've gone on diets, taken nutritional courses, and worked with my life coach to help me see food as a friend, not a foe. For the longest time, I was an emotional eater. I ate when I was sad. I ate when I was happy. I ate when I was angry. It wasn't until I learned to eat with awareness and to eat mindfully that I learned to use food to provide my body with nutrients, not to numb my feelings. I learned I must nourish my body in order to flourish.

I used to fuel my body the way I'd fuel my car—I waited until the tank was almost empty. The gas gauge tried to warn me, but I ignored it until the very last minute. Late for work, I filled up under duress, and caused myself unnecessary worry and anxiety. I had to realize how much easier it was to fill up my tank sooner—to not take a chance of running out of gas and damaging the engine. Then my car and I stopped running on fumes.

Over the years, I learned to appreciate food for what it could do for my body. Then I chose foods based on their nutritional value, rather than as a tool to avoid my feelings or to-do list. I paid attention to which foods made me feel tired and which gave me energy. I kept a food journal to determine which foods filled me up faster and which foods left me feeling hungry.

Food became a self care tool. Now I eat at a slower pace and serve myself smaller portions. I give my stomach time to tell my brain it's full. I use smaller plates, eat three meals a day, and arrange the food by color on a pretty plate so it's pleasing to the eye. I eat at the dining room table instead of at my desk. I think about where the food comes from, the farmer who grew it, and the truck driver who got it to the store.

Little by little when I changed my relationship with food, I saw it as something I use for fuel and to keep my body running at its best. I stopped using food as something just to provide comfort or an escape. Now I fill up with healthy foods and use mealtime as another self care tool

Quick Action Step:

Write down one thing
you'll do today to nourish your body

_____

_____

Believe

· · · · · · · · · ·

Day 7:
Believe in
Your Power

Even if you choose to give someone the power to write your story for you, you can always take back the pen. —Sandra Cooze

. . . .

I learned to own my personal power and become confident in my self care journey over many years. By trial and error, I came to believe I own my story and can take back the pen, like the time I returned a pair of shoes.

The shoes were stunning black leather stilettos, but I decided they didn't fit the outfit I had originally chosen them for. I approached the saleswoman and explained I wanted a refund. With a sly grin on her face, she snickered, "Oh yes, these shoes are way too hot and sexy for you."

I immediately felt insecure. I had come into the store after a workout in my yoga-clothes-no-make-up-running-errands look. Then this stranger made me question my beauty. Her words stung in a way that made me go to a dark place. I thought, "She's right, I am not hot and sexy and would never have looked good in these shoes."

I gave away my power.

After a few minutes of sitting in my car wallowing in self-pity, I made a conscious choice to take back my power. I tapped into my self care tool belt and embraced who I was. This woman would not ruin my day. I would not be a victim of someone else's insensitivity.

I went back into the store.

With a smile on my face and without anger, I said, "I have to let you know I felt hurt by what you said, and I would like to believe that was not your intention." I didn't want to get even. I wanted to communicate my feelings about the situation.

She said no, she didn't mean to be hurtful. In fact, she meant to be funny, and when I didn't laugh, she knew she should have apologized, but then she was too afraid and embarrassed to do so. She thanked me for coming back in and for giving her a chance to fix the awkward situation she had created. She said she was sorry. The conversation lasted less than 5 minutes and ended in a hug.

I took back the pen and rewrote my story without putting her down or embarrassing her. I made the choice to stand up to this woman. I stopped complaining and feeling sorry for myself. I forgave her and believed her intentions were good.

When it was all over, I felt empowered and confident that even without those shoes, I was one hot and sexy woman.

Quick Action Step:

Believe you have the power.
Write down one thing you'll do today
to take back your power.

_____

_____

Practice

makes progress.

~ Reggie Adams

Practice

Day 8:
Practice Self Love by Filling Your Goodness Container

You yourself, as much as anybody in the entire universe,
deserve your love and affection. —Buddha

. . . .

Each spring in Arizona where I live, the saguaro cacti become plump from the winter rains. They stretch their arms wide and puff up with a sense of importance. This reminds me of something I call my goodness container—a part of my heart that stores all the good stuff I do for myself. Keeping this invisible receptacle filled to the brim plays a significant role in my self care journey.

The saguaros are perfect examples of good self care. They know they must store as much moisture as they can because there will be dry, barren times. The desert here averages just seven inches of rain a year. These prickly giants absorb and store considerable amounts of rainwater, visibly expanding in the process. Then they use the stored water as needed, which enables these towering succulents to survive during extended periods of drought.

Are you storing as much goodness as possible so you can withstand a future drought? Are you filling your goodness container with positive affirmations and kind, loving thoughts? Are you pampering yourself? Do you limit your exposure to the news, spend time in nature, avoid toxic people, and extend yourself grace?

I liken it to my bank account. When I make regular deposits into my goodness container by showing myself respect and kindness, there is an abundance of respect and kindness available for me when I need it most. My goodness container is my rainy-day fund.

One way I make deposits into my rainy-day fund is when I send myself metta, a Sanskrit word meaning loving kindness. I repeat a mantra a few times silently or out loud, "May I be happy. May I be healthy. May I be at peace."

Practicing self love means treating ourselves as we do our children, our spouses, and our friends when they need help. I mail notes to friends to lift their spirits and let them know I'm thinking of them. So why not send myself a note? It may seem awkward at first, but it gets easier. And when I practice compassion toward myself, the easier it is to quiet those ugly voices in my head that say I'm not worthy, I'm not good enough, I'm not loved.

What are you longing to hear? Make it a habit to say it to yourself. Write it down on a post-it note or pretty stationary. Speak to your heart directly and fill it up with all the love and attention and support it aches for.

When the mighty Sonoran Desert saguaros are fully hydrated, they can weigh up to 4,800 pounds. That's a lot of goodness. How much self love do you need to get through the droughts in your life? Which of these self care tips will you use to make deposits into your goodness container so on those dry days, there will be plenty of love to go around?

Quick Action Step:

Practice self love.
Write below one thing you can do today
to fill your goodness container.

_____

_____

Practice

· · · · · · · · · ·

Day 9:
Practice Smiling

Peace begins with a smile. —Mother Teresa

. . . .

I learned early in my self care journey a simple smile can change my day. I could be in the lowest of moods when a cheerful face or friendly hello from a stranger in the line at the coffee shop could bring me out of my debilitating sadness. Then I realized I didn't have to wait to receive this powerful gift from someone else. I could give it to myself.

Smiles are the ultimate self care tool.

What is a smile? It's just a slight curl at the ends of my mouth, which turns something on in my mind and heart. It feels peaceful. I like it. In less than a second, I can be uplifted.

At first, it seemed awkward and fake. But the more I practiced, the easier it got—and the more I received in return.

Smiles are contagious.

Have you noticed how often someone will reciprocate a smile after you share one? There's a scientific explanation for the phenomenon. According to neuroscientist Marco Iacoboni, we all possess something called mirror neurons. When we perform an action, or even witness someone in motion, these cells are activated. And when we smile, mirror neurons respond to the acts of both seeing and doing.

Experts report smiling can reduce your heart rate, help you recover from stress, and retrain your brain to create happiness loops that encourage positive thinking patterns. This positive facial expression can boost our moods, release negative thoughts, and increase productivity and creativity.

Now I wave and smile at cars I pass in the neighborhood or when I'm out for a walk. I hope it uplifts my neighbors. I know it uplifts me.

Smiles are something I can use to add a touch of self care to my day. They take little effort and I can do them anytime. They give me a sense of peace and they cost nothing—definitely something to smile about.

Quick Action Step:

Practice smiling right now.
Write on the lines below one positive
feeling you experienced from smiling.

_____

_____

Practice

· · · · · · · · · ·

Day 10:
Practice Meditation

It is indeed a radical act of love just to sit down and
be quiet for a time by yourself. —Jon Kabat-Zinn

. . . .

My meditation practice didn't happen for me overnight. I was introduced to it at my yoga studio. Then my doctor recommended it to help me sleep. Also, Weight Watchers suggested it would help with weight loss. I heard about the benefits of meditation from several sources, and I was intrigued. Okay, maybe I was desperate? Either way, I was ready to try this new experience many people insisted could transform my life.

I started small. I took a one-hour beginner's class every Sunday for my first year. The instructor led us through 10–15-minute meditations, and then we discussed how that went and what came up for us. We did this 3–4 times in each class. For 60 minutes a week, I practiced the new discipline.

I didn't see a difference at first, but I liked the feeling of sacred quietude I experienced during the class. The instructor introduced us to all types: walking, silent, and guided. He suggested we empty our minds of our "to-do" lists and our worries and reminded us to keep coming back to our breath. And then he suggested when a thought came up, we could mentally label it "a thought," and return to our breath.

This was difficult. The errands I needed to run after class or the argument I had with someone earlier continued to surface. But when I acknowledged those thoughts, labeled them, and said good-bye to them, I was lulled into a state of lightness, a feeling of peace, and a sense of wonder about what lies beneath the surface of my mind.

Ten years later, I now have a self care tool that has transformed my life. Meditation sustains me, empowers me, and provides calm when I need it most. I have used it to prepare for difficult conversations. I have used it while getting a root canal, while waiting for word of my husband's surgery, and while getting a special type of mammogram that kept me in the "grip of death" for over 10 minutes.

This new discipline has helped me respond to situations with grace rather than react with anger. Since I have learned to quiet my mind and focus on my breath, I navigate life through a clearer lens—a lens magnified with love, acceptance, and compassion. When I need a pick-me-up in the middle of the afternoon, instead of reaching for caffeine or sugar, I reach for my timer, set it for 5 minutes, and concentrate on my breath. Closing my eyes and sitting still can help me feel refreshed and invigorated.

Of course, one does not learn this self care tool in just a few sessions, and maybe that's why people don't do it. It takes time to reap the benefits. Sometimes I forget just how much it helps me until I go a few days without practicing. I become irritable or wake up often at night. My doctor was right. These techniques quiet my brain, calm my nerves, release my worries, and are more effective than counting sheep.

Here's a simple way to get started:

1. Set a timer for 5 minutes.

2. Find a comfortable place and sit with your back straight. It's important you are not lying down or slouching as you might fall asleep. Close the door and silence your phone so no one will disturb you.

3. Let your hands rest naturally and comfortably in your lap or on top of each other.

4. Close your eyes or gaze softly toward the floor.

5. Start breathing deeply and fully, eventually to a natural breathing rhythm.

6. Focus on your breath and nothing else.

7. When a thought comes, acknowledge the thought, let it pass, and go back to focusing on the rhythm of your breathing.

Don't judge. Thoughts will come and go. You can't turn off your brain, but you can guide it. This is what meditation is—the return to the breath, over and over again—and it takes a lot of practice.

It is indeed a radical act of love just to sit down and be quiet for a time by yourself. Isn't it time to show yourself you are worth it?

Quick Action Step:

Write on the following lines one thing
you will do today to explore meditation.
You might google local classes, check out apps like
Insight Timer, Headspace, or Ten Percent Happier,
or try the 7 steps listed above.

_____

_____

· · · · · · · · · ·

Day 11:
Practice Setting
a Daily Intention

Our intention creates our reality. —Dr. Wayne Dyer

. . . .

In the early Arizona morning, I walk my heart-shaped labyrinth and meditate with the sound of gold finches and cactus wrens in the background. The sun is just coming up, and it is lighting my path surrounded by graceful paloverde and majestic mesquite trees. I cherish this precious quietude before my day begins. It is the perfect way to wake up my senses, create an awareness of openness, and set my intention for the new day.

You don't need a labyrinth to create your own routine for starting your day. All you need is a willingness to set aside a small amount of time first thing in the morning. Give yourself alone time that allows you to be grateful, to take stock of your life, or to prepare to make this day your best one yet.

When I first began my self care journey, getting out of bed was one of the hardest things I did in my day. I recall a feeling of dread come over me as I thought about all the things on my to-do list.

Then, my life coach encouraged me to create a daily intention. I started small. At first it was just to get out of bed. The secret was to acknowledge myself for doing it and give myself credit.

After a few days, I was ready to try something bigger. I made the intention to track my water intake to ensure I was getting enough hydration. After a week, my intention was to exercise for 15 minutes three times a week. I celebrated each time I achieved my intention. If I didn't make it, I said to myself, "I will try again tomorrow."

This practice cemented my belief in the power of setting intentions and created a discipline which supports my self care journey.

My labyrinth and the early morning ritual took years to come about. It was a process of slowly, but diligently, expanding my tools for self care. You can create your own habit by declaring an intention, finding your special space, and designing your own unique way to tell yourself you matter.

Quick Action Step:

Write down one intention for today.
Make your bed? Eat breakfast?
Get outside and walk for 10 minutes?
Sit down, close your eyes, and be silent for 5 minutes?

_____

_____

Practice

· · · · · · · · · ·

Day 12:
Practice the
Healing Power of Yoga

Yoga isn't about touching your toes.
It's about what you learn on the way down there. —Jigar Gor

. . . .

After my mom's long illness and death, I began a journey of retrospection and self-discovery. I realized the preciousness of life and the delicacy of love, and I searched for balance by simplifying my work, my life, and my relationships. It was during this time my yoga practice became a lifeline for healing.

Contrary to popular belief, yoga is not a religion, and it's not just for vegetarian hippies. Yoga is for everyone at any level and can fit into every lifestyle. It's not just about curling up into pretzel-like positions or chanting for hours at a time. Yoga can be a self care tool which encourages you to slow down, listen to your body, and begin the healing process.

And it is a practice.

At first, I took only beginner classes. Then I tried restorative yoga to enjoy the restful and less strenuous side of the practice. It didn't take me long to see yoga is helpful to both my physical and mental well-being. All the flexing, bending, and stretching was a challenge—and I was lengthening parts of my body I didn't know existed. That's when it became "all the stuff I was learning about myself on the way down to touching my toes."

Yes, yoga is a great source of exercise. But it is also a melding of mind, body, and spirit. Now, I am aware of my body and what it's trying to say to me. I practice going to my edge, and I listen to what my body is telling me today. Each day, I have different limits and different lessons to be learned. On my mat, I practice the release of roles: mother, wife, volunteer, and friend. I inhabit the role of student. I let go of shoulds, woulds, and coulds, and embrace possibilities.

The lessons I learned on the mat also transferred to my life off the mat. I've learned to be less critical of myself and cut myself some slack. I've learned to resist less and soften more. I've learned to ease into life even when the current feels as though it is going against me. Now I am kinder to myself and give myself grace.

I've practiced all types of yoga: restorative, power, flow, partner, Hatha, Iyengar, and hot Bikram. Even in chair yoga, you can practice the healing power of yoga by breathing deeply and completely, which is critical to a healthy mind and body.

As I've aged, I've had to change the type of yoga I practice, but I keep going back. In every season of my life, I found the right yoga classes for my type of body, my individual exercise goals, and my level of skill. Experts agree yoga helps manage stress, ease depression and anxiety, improve mood, and enhance the quality of sleep. In addition, yoga has been shown to increase flexibility, improve balance and coordination, reduce pain, and increase strength. I've experienced all of that and more.

Whether in a local studio, online at Glo.com, YogaRove.com, or Giam.com, or with a borrowed DVD from the library, practice the healing power of yoga today and see how it can support your self care journey. You may never touch your toes, but you will learn about your body, mind, and spirit.

Quick Action Step:

Schedule a time to look at one of the websites listed above or decide when you will call your local yoga studio. Write when you will do this below.

_____

_____

Day 13:
Practice Good
Sleep Habits

Sleep is that golden chain that ties health and our bodies together. —Thomas Dekker

. . . .

As I've aged, a good night's sleep has become elusive. And when I don't rest well, I don't live well. If I don't get enough shut-eye, it affects my mood, my energy, and my attitude. The simplest of tasks, like getting out of bed, can overwhelm me.

Sleep is critical for good self care—and when you make it a priority, it can be one of the best things you do for your health and well-being. When you get enough rest, you're less likely to get sick, you are more likely to maintain a healthy weight, and you lower your risk for serious problems like diabetes and heart disease.

When I chose to tackle my insomnia, I tracked those things that had either a positive or a negative effect on my time in bed. I used an app on my phone called CBTi-coach, but a piece of paper and pen are just as good. I tracked exercise, TV watching, alcohol consumption, minutes of meditation, pages journaled, caffeine and sugar intake, and the number of nights I used sleep aids.

It didn't take me long to see the choices I made during the day and especially, right before bed, affected how I would sleep at night. As a result, my daily goals are to drink less caffeine, eat less sugar, and avoid naps—and I strive to get exercise, drink water, and meditate. Before bed, I watch less TV and stay off my phone. Proactively, I take baths, drink chamomile tea, and meditate.

Meditation is now my favorite defense against insomnia.

I've read meditation can help make our sleep patterns more predictable and cause the release of melatonin. If my eyes refuse to close or my mind refuses to shut down, I don't get angry and think, "I might as well start to plan my day and create my to-do list." Instead, I choose to get comfortable, lie still, and focus on my breath. I switch into a mindfulness mode versus a worry, anger, or frustration mode.

A good night's rest is within my grasp when I stick to the same bedtime schedule, pay attention to what I eat and drink, exercise, stay hydrated, create a restful environment in my bedroom, and meditate. My time in bed becomes less about counting sheep and more about the deep slumber I crave. I practice good sleep habits and strengthen the golden chain that ties health and my body together.

Quick Action Step:

Write down one thing
you'll do today to sleep well tonight.

_____

_____

Practice

· · · · · · · · · · ·

Day 14:
Practice Setting Boundaries

Daring to set boundaries is about having the courage to love ourselves,
even when we risk disappointing others. —Brene Brown

. . . .

I recently had a conversation with a friend about boundaries and saying "No." Her phone was ringing and as a successful realtor, her phone rings a lot. But we were having girlfriend time, and she was torn between interrupting our special coffee break together and working.

"I don't want to answer it, but it might be my client who just received his pre-qualification approval, and he probably just wants to talk about it."

I asked her, "Are you working now or not?"

She paused, looked at the ringing phone, and said, "I guess I'm not working."

Whether you work outside the home, are a full-time parent, a caregiver, or retired, knowing when to say yes and when to say no is an important part of self care. Unfortunately, though, it is often the last thing we think about. It was hard for my friend to say no to the call. She hadn't set clear boundaries for herself regarding her schedule nor whether she would be at the mercy of her customers 24/7. She hadn't yet created defined times for when she was working and when she was not.

I created boundaries years ago after taking a Calendar Can-Do Course from Life Coach Reggie Adams. I learned how important it is to schedule "me-time"—actually writing it on my calendar. Yes, my doctor appointments and manicures were on my calendar, but now I add to my calendar fun things (bubble baths or walks) and not-so-fun chores (grocery shopping or paying the bills).

I planned and scheduled all those things I was not getting done in my life. When I practiced setting boundaries, the important tasks got done—and if a client, friend, or family member asked if I was available, my quick and honest reply was, "No." When I asked them to consider another date and offered convenient times for me and them, it was a win-win for everyone. I could be there without resentment for all the other people who relied on me. This wasn't about lying or being inflexible. This was about self-preservation and making sure I took care of myself.

When you practice setting boundaries with your time, relationships, and feelings, you may end up saying "No" a lot. Not a problem.

And once you learn to say it regularly in your daily life, the easier it is to say, "Yes" to self care.

Quick Action Step:

Write below and then add to your calendar
one "me-time" activity you never have time for.
How about make a cup of tea, light a candle, and listen
to your favorite music? Or get outside, sit in the garden,
and take a nap in your favorite lawn chair?

_____

_____

Life is a matter of choices
and every choice you make,

makes you.

~ John C. Maxwell

WEEK THREE

Choose

Choose

· · · · · · · · · ·

Day 15:
Choose Joy

Watch your thoughts; they become words. Watch your words; they become actions.
Watch your actions; they become habit. Watch your habits; they become character.
Watch your character; it becomes your destiny. —Lao Tzu

. . . .

When I closed my business after 15 years and moved to Arizona to retire, I knew one thing I wanted most in life was an abundance of joy. So, I opened a new email address and ordered my new Arizona license plate—both with the words "Choose Joy." I was determined to add joy to my self care tool belt.

Positivity has played a huge role in getting me through tough times and taking care of myself. But what if seeing the sunny side of things doesn't come easily for you? Don't worry. It can be learned. And when you look for the joy in a situation, joy will return to you.

Watch your thoughts; they become words.

Self-talk is a great place to start to increase your positivity. I look for the joy in everything and everywhere. A sunny day. A cool breeze. The first bite of a sweet, ripe mango. A hard-to-get parking spot. A balanced checkbook. The right result for a medical test. A note from a friend. Every time something works out well or provides me with pleasure, I celebrate. With each pure delight, I say to myself, "Joy is everywhere."

Watch your words; they become actions.

The words we choose will impact how the world responds. When I'm having a bad day and finding fault in those around me, negativity can become a self-fulfilling prophecy. The energy I put out into the world is the energy I get back. I use a mantra for bad days. "I flow through life with peace and ease." I am gentle with myself and repeat the mantra out loud.

Watch your actions; they become habit.

Our posture can communicate a lot to both the outside world and to ourselves. Stand up straight with your chin held high—and tell the world you are a positive force to be reckoned with. Smile. Spend time with optimistic people. It's taken me years to realize how important it is to eliminate toxic relationships and avoid negative people. These people zap my energy and make it difficult for me to feel joy. Begin a new practice to stand tall and surround yourself with joyful souls.

Watch your habits; they become character, and your character becomes your destiny.

I've read researchers continue to explore the effects of positive thinking and optimism on health. They include increased life span, less depression, reduced levels of stress, increased resistance to the common cold, increased psychological and physical well-being, improved cardiovascular health, and improved coping skills during hardships and times of stress.

When you choose joy, you see the brighter side of life. You find the good in a situation so you can be happy, healthy, and whole. It doesn't mean you put your head in the sand and ignore the problem. It means you expect the best outcome and manage stress with resilience, grace, and courage.

Bring joy into your life. Create a destiny filled with possibilities, hope, and lots of self care.

Quick Action Step:

Write one thing you can celebrate today,
or one person who did something nice for you,
or one characteristic you love about yourself.

_____

_____

Choose

· · · · · · · · · ·

Day 16:
Choose Resilience

Fall down seven times, get up eight. —Japanese Proverb

. . . .

Resilience was a primary goal of mine when I first started my self care journey. I wanted to respond quickly to all types of stress: physical, emotional, and mental. It wasn't a matter of if life would get stressful as I got older. It was a matter of when it would get stressful and how I would respond to stress.

I was exhausted from juggling my role as caretaker for my parents, along with all the other responsibilities of being a mom, wife, business owner, and volunteer. Because I overextended myself almost every day, my body remained in the fight-or-flight mode. Suffering from the physical toll of continuous periods of stress and in constant crisis mode, I had no idea what was going on inside my body.

In times of stress, the body mobilizes every resource it has available to help you get through those situations, but if you never allow yourself to heal, recover, and process those events, your system will continue to think you are still stressed. Unless you intervene, your body will continue to be compromised. Eventually, it will break down and stop functioning at healthy levels.

Each time you react habitually to stress in unhealthy ways, you reduce your intrinsic capacity for well-being and balance. Many times, you are unaware of the patterns you have fallen into and their consequences. Adrenal glands pump out adrenaline and cortisol just like when you are in life-threatening situations, but your body can't decipher between the stress of fleeing the saber-toothed tiger or doing your taxes. So it reacts the same way, causing your body to digest food inefficiently, to lose focus and forget things, to stop eliminating toxins, or to stop your immune system from functioning optimally.

No wonder I was feeling exhausted, had back pain, muscle pain, headaches, and couldn't sleep or function well. My body was retaliating from constant stress.

A great first step to building resilience is to start your self care journey. Choose a life filled with meditation, mindfulness, and regular exercise—and build resilience. Surround yourself with positive people, get enough sleep, and eat well—and build resilience.

The stresses of life don't have to jeopardize your health. Instead, use self care to create a life you love.

Quick Action Step:

Write below one way you can
build your resistance today.
Choose meditating for 5 minutes, stretching,
or practicing box breathing (Day 3)

_____

_____

Choose

· · · · · · · · · ·

Day 17:
Choose Forgiveness

When a deep injury is done to us, we never heal until we forgive. —Nelson Mandela

. . . .

I have many people in my life whom I've worked hard to forgive. I used to get upset, angry, and hold a grudge when a co-worker took credit for my work, a friend stopped returning my calls, or a family member hurt my feelings. Then I discovered forgiveness gave me peace. With each act of forgiveness, I willed my way towards an act of love for both the person I forgave and for myself. I added forgiveness to my self care tool belt.

Forgiveness is an important self care tool.

Forgiveness is about extending grace to those we perceive have caused us pain, including ourselves. It isn't about forgetting what happened or excusing the behavior. Forgiveness means letting go of the hostility, hurt, and the desire for vengeance. We have a choice to accept what has happened in the past is an old story, recognize that people make mistakes, and continue forward with empathy. When you liberate yourself from the pain and anxiety of what happened, you move away from debilitating anger and resentment before they have time to seep inside and spoil the rest of your life.

Each time I've been able to forgive, I've felt a weight released from my shoulders. I've experienced a freedom from the outrage and frustration wrapped around my heart. When I forgive, I can love. When I love, I heal.

I learned to forgive with small acts of mercy for myself. When I make a mistake or speak unkindly in the heat of anger, I remind myself I'm human and I send myself love. When

I extend grace to me, it's easier to extend grace to those I feel have caused me pain. When I show empathy toward myself, I'm likely to do the same toward others.

Years ago, I was in an abusive relationship with a pathological liar. Forgiveness played a big role in why this experience didn't have more of a negative impact on my life. When I discovered to what degree I had been betrayed, I could have been devastated. Instead, I chose to forgive myself and move forward. I took action: kicked the guy out and ended the relationship. I took responsibility for the part I played, accepted this person—with whom I had chosen to be in relationship with—was mentally unstable, and I gave myself grace.

Forgiveness is easier when I hold on to compassion and patience.

I don't mean to diminish the immense challenge forgiveness can be and I realize this might be the toughest tip in this book. But I also realize the powerful tool it is for our self care. When we hold on to hurt, pain, and distrust, we give our power away to the situation or to the person who caused it. When we allow the toxicity of bitterness into our lives, we are not being our best selves.

It took a long time to forgive the pathological liar, but because I did, I grew from the experience instead of allowing it to stop me from being my best self.

I've read when we forgive, there are strong psychological benefits for us. Forgiveness can lead to stronger relationships, improved mental health, less anxiety, less stress, less hostility, lower blood pressure, fewer symptoms of depression, a stronger immune system, improved heart health, and improved self-esteem.

Start with yourself. Did you eat the entire bag of chips on the first day of your new diet? Forgive yourself. Did you take a nap when you should have walked the dog? Forgive yourself. Did you speak unkind words to a loved one? Forgive yourself.

When you choose to forgive and take action to live your best life, you can find peace and joy. Then you can let the amazing transformation begin. Let the black clouds of anxiety and depression give way to enhanced self-esteem and genuine feelings of hopefulness. Choose forgiveness—and choose to contribute to your own healing.

Quick Action Step:

Choose one thing you will forgive yourself
or someone else for today. Write it below.

_____

_____

Choose

· · · · · · · · · ·

Day 18:
Choose to Let Go

Letting go is freedom, and freedom is the only condition for happiness. —Thich Nhat Hanh

. . . .

When we choose to let go, it means we choose to let things be. Letting go means we stop holding onto the need to have things be a certain way. We stop causing ourselves pain. When we let go, we open the doorway to freedom.

A key element of mindfulness, letting go may be the toughest tip to describe. But it is one of the most important self care tips in this book. When we choose to let go, we support our acceptance of the way things are and create a foundation for a life of joy and abundance.

While I cared for my elderly parents, I wished things were not as they were. I wished Mom and Dad were healthier. I wished I had extra help. I wished I had additional hours in the day.

I was attached to the idea things should be different from what they were. I obsessed. I worried. I fumed. I caused myself needless pain.

Through yoga, meditation, and working with my life coach, I learned to let go of the scenario I thought I should have and accept the reality. I had two loving parents, a supportive family, access to community services, and helpful friends.

During my journey toward a healthy weight, I learned to be mindful and present while eating and thinking about food. For instance, before I became mindful, I rushed through my meals while checking email or when I stood at the kitchen sink. Now I sit at the table, focus on each bite, and appreciate the tastes and textures and how the food gives me energy and keeps me healthy.

Once I stopped holding onto the picture I had created of what I should look like and the type of body I should have at my age, I could make different choices with less struggle about what I ate. Then the journey became easier.

At first, this concept of letting go eluded me. My anger, frustration, and all the stress I was under hindered my attempts to think differently. One way I practice is with mantras like "I release my anger" and "I will let go of my frustration today." Or in a positive light, I affirm, "I have all I need to be happy, healthy, and whole." To randomly incorporate the practice of letting go throughout my day, I repeat my mantra each time I touch a door handle. Every time I open a door, I experience an increased sense of freedom and happiness.

In my daily meditation sittings, I release thoughts, judgments, fears, and worries. The past and future melt away, and I watch with curiosity and compassion in the present moment. There's a deep feeling of joy, surrender, and independence when I can let go of whatever does not serve me.

When I practice yoga or meditation, or write in my journal, I encourage my mind to release negativity, fear, and unhappiness. It may only be for a few seconds at a time—similar to touching a door handle—but for those few seconds, I feel a rush of liberation.

For a short time, I know the relief of being enough, being accepted, and being loved.

Research on the brain shows the hardest thing for the brain to do is to let go of thoughts. Don't be critical of yourself if this seems difficult to do. This practice supports acceptance of the way things are and nurtures qualities of authenticity, self-compassion, and resilience. Learning to let go of the things not serving you will free up energy and resources, and you will begin to reap the benefits of a grateful and joyful life. The rewards are worth it.

Choose to let go. Choose self care. Choose a life filled with freedom and happiness.

Quick Action Step:

Write your mantra, "Today I let go of ..."

_____

_____

Choose

· · · · · · · · · ·

Day 19:
Choose to
Explore Nature

In every walk with nature, one receives far more than one seeks. —John Muir

. . . .

When I was growing up in a rural township in northeastern Ohio, I would get on my hand-me-down bicycle, rush to the bottom of our steep driveway, race along the not-so-well-paved road and fly away. Fulfilling a secret dream, I imagined my bike was a horse, and I whispered to my handlebars, "Fly, horsey, fly!" I tasted the sense of freedom I yearned for when I heard the crunch of the gravel under my tires and felt the crisp wind against my face.

I boldly journeyed out onto the streets of my tiny town, beyond the safety of my home. I might venture across the railroad tracks, past the downtown square, and ride for miles. No matter how far I went, I felt like I was escaping it all. I was in charge of my life, and nothing could stop me from being whomever or whatever I wanted to be.

Over the years on my self care journey, I have looked for ways to recreate a feeling of reckless abandon. I've sought experiences which would help me feel open, hopeful, and full of joy, just like I did when I was a kid.

The one place I have been able to find a sense of freedom most often is in nature. I've always been able to connect with my inner child when hiking among the trees, standing in a garden, or sitting on a beach. What is it about the great outdoors that makes me feel unscheduled, unconfined, and unrestrained?

There's plenty of scientific research which verifies the physical, cognitive, and mental benefits of spending time in nature. These include improved short-term memory, restored mental energy, immediate stress relief, and enhanced creativity. Spending time outside can reduce inflammation, sharpen our thinking, improve concentration, and boost our immune system. No wonder I feel so good after a hike in the Arizona desert near my home.

Experts also believe being where you can smell fresh air, see endless blue skies, or bask in the warm sun allows us to drop our roles in life. We don't need to be spouse, boss, parent, or caregiver while taking a stroll around the block, sitting on our back patio, or taking the dog for a walk. The trees, flowers, birds, and bugs don't stress about their roles in life, and maybe just being among them gives us permission to show up as our true selves—and for a short time, release our responsibilities and relax. The river and the rocks don't care who we are or what we say to them. Without the judgments of the everyday world, we can be fully present and free to be whomever or whatever we wish to be.

Let's explore nature for self care. We'll receive more than we seek.

Quick Action Step:

Schedule a time today
to go outside for fresh air or
sit near a window and enjoy the view.
Write it below.

_____

_____

Choose

· · · · · · · · · ·

Day 20:
Choose an Attitude
of Gratitude

If you concentrate on what you have, you'll always have more.
If you concentrate on what you don't have, you'll never have enough. —Lewis Howes

. . . .

Are you a glass-half-empty kind of person? You know the type. He or she is always sharing too much about their latest physical ailment, relationship woes, or how unfair life has been to them. You want to be nice and help somehow, but after a while, you realize their negativity is bringing you down. A tool I use to channel optimism, and a cornerstone of my self care journey, is an attitude of gratitude.

I admit, I don't always practice what I preach. I can be a glass-half-empty person by telling myself, "What's happening right now is all my fault." As an example, if I get sick, my first thoughts are often, "What a fool, Carole! You felt this cold coming on and did nothing about it. You shouldn't have eaten so much sugar and you should have gone back to bed. You're supposed to be the queen of self care. How could you let yourself get sick?"

It's times like these, I need to be as positive as possible. Going down the rabbit hole of negative mind chatter will only make me sicker.

So I go to my gratitude journal and start writing. I am grateful it's a cold, not pneumonia. I am grateful for modern meds and that I can use them. I am grateful I have a can of chicken soup in the pantry. I am grateful for my friends and family who have been checking in with me and asking if I need anything.

By the time I write everything I am grateful for, I've stopped being so hard on myself and I have a smile on my face.

Recent studies show when we take a few moments to pause and be grateful, we switch from the sympathetic (fight-or-flight) to the parasympathetic (growth and repair) nervous system. In fight or flight, the blood leaves the organs and goes to the extremities, and our heart and respiratory rate are on alert. A quick shift into growth and repair aids digestion, promotes healing, improves heart health, and strengthens our immune system.

If the gratitude process is hard to get started, ask yourself, "What could I be grateful for?" Imagine what you wish for and write the outcome you want from your current circumstance. When I'm sick, I describe in my journal a day where I am healthy, happy, and whole with energy to do everything I want. My perspective changes immediately. I may still have a cold or flu, but my attitude has shifted from negative to positive, and I feel better.

Find a pretty notebook or journal to write your thoughts. The power of the written word cannot be underestimated.

I also keep a notebook at my bedside to write three things I'm grateful for before I turn out the light. On bad days, when I find it hard to be grateful for anything, I stick with the basics. I am grateful for my bed. I am grateful for my pajamas. I am grateful for electricity and running water. I am grateful for the roof over my head. I am grateful for my attitude of gratitude.

Gratitude is a low-cost self care tool and takes only a few minutes. Choose an attitude of gratitude and you'll always have more.

Quick Action Step:

Write below one thing you are grateful for and why.

_____

_____

Choose

· · · · · · · · · ·

Day 21:
Choose to List
Ways to Love Yourself

No woman can control her destiny if she doesn't give
TO herself as much as she gives OF herself. —Suze Orman

. . . .

In the last few years of my elderly parents' lives, I woke up often in the middle of the night by a call from one of them saying the other was on the way to the emergency room. I would pack a bag and head out the door, leaving my husband wide awake with instructions for getting our young daughter off to school. That was my life. I was running a business, volunteering at school, being the perfect mom, wife—and in charge of my parents' health and well-being.

On one of those nights when I arrived at the hospital, I was escorted to my father's room. Dad lay there in the dimly lit space with his eyes closed. He appeared tiny in this huge hospital bed surrounded by machines, tubes, and wires. The scene was all too familiar. I felt lost and as hopeless as Dad looked.

It was times such as these when depression reared its ugly head and consumed me. Feelings of despair, and the fear I couldn't handle anything else would sweep over me with great force. I would often resort to pushing through it with anger—and I would yell at anyone in my path—or by going back to bed. I knew I had to find another way.

My life coach gave me the idea to list ways to love myself, which encouraged me to brainstorm ways to pamper myself. I started out with just a few ideas. Over the years,

I have added to it. I refer to this list whenever I need to remind myself I matter—I am worthy of love. The items I put on my list can be simple and take less than 5 minutes. Or I create more involved treats for myself. The choice is yours.

Here are examples from my list:

1. Buy Yourself Flowers (the next time you're at the grocery store)
2. Practice Yoga (even if you only have time for 10 minutes of sun salutations)
3. Eat a Healthy Snack (Make it pretty. Sit down to enjoy it)
4. Read a Book (curled up on the couch in your fuzzy red socks)
5. Scrapbook (look at your photos)
6. Write a Letter (maybe to yourself)
7. Sing Loud and Proud in the Shower or Car
8. Take a Long Hot Bath
9. Get a Manicure or Give Yourself One
10. Go for a Walk
11. Go Swimming and Get Your Hair Wet
12. Call a Good Friend and Just Chat

13. Make Yourself a Cup of Coffee/Tea/Hot Chocolate

14. Light a Candle

15. Call a Friend for a Lunch Date

16. Watch Old Seinfeld Reruns or Any Other Show That Will Make You LAUGH

17. Use Your Special China Even Though It Isn't a Holiday

18. Listen to Music

19. Write in Your Favorite Journal

20. Watch an Old Movie

21. Take a Nap

22. Get a Facial or Give Yourself One

23. Write a Short Poem to Yourself

Take control of your destiny and give TO yourself as much as you give OF yourself.

Quick Action Step:

Start your own List of Ways to Love Yourself
using the following pages.
Begin with one or two items and build it over time.
Your first item could be,
Create or add to my "Ways to Love Myself" list.

Post it on your refrigerator.
Refer to it often.
Discover the power of pampering yourself.
and showing yourself simple acts of love.

Ways to Love Yourself:

1. _____

2. _____

3. _____

4. _____

5. _____

6. _____

7. _____

8. _____

9. _____

10. _____

11. _____

12. _____

13. _____

14. _____

15. _____

16. _____

17. _____

18. _____

19. _____

20. _____

21. _____

22. _____

23. _____

Note From the Author

· · · · · · · · ·

I wrote this book during the COVID-19 pandemic. These self care tips, and my willingness to make self care a priority, got me through the isolation, deprivation, and frightening unknowns so many of us experienced during that time.

My hope for you is that from reading these tips over the past 21 days, taking the action steps, and hearing my story, you have begun your own self care journey. When you BELIEVE in, PRACTICE, and CHOOSE the gift of self care you can have the life you desire and the life you deserve.

I'd love to hear about your journey and which techniques worked best for you. Please share your thoughts with me at www.fuzzyredsocks.com.

Resources

· · · · · · · · ·

The following are individuals whose work and ideas inspired and guided me on my self care journey. They are listed alphabetically.

Reggie Adams, CEO and Founder of Reggie's Coaching Academy, which serves thousands of clients from all over the world and remains a pioneer in the very popular GUTS and Immersion Programs. Reggie earned her Life Coach certification from The Coaches Training Institute and enjoys using her training and knowledge to journey with others on a path of balance, purpose, and peace.
https://www.reggiescoachingacademy.com/

Blake D. Bauer, Inspirational speaker, alternative medicine practitioner, and author of *You Were Not Born to Suffer*. Watkins Publishing, UK and USA, 2017.
https://www.unconditional-selflove.com/

Brené Brown, Ph.D., LMSW, research professor at the University of Houston-Graduate College of Social Work. She studies vulnerability, courage, worthiness, and shame. Her TEDx Houston talk on the power of vulnerability is one of the most watched talks on TED.com, with over 15 million views.
https://brenebrown.com/

Jon Kabat-Zinn, PhD, internationally known for his work as a scientist, writer, and mindfulness meditation teacher. Kabat-Zinn developed the formal mindfulness practices. Jon's dedication has brought mindfulness-based stress reduction (MBSR), into the mainstream of medicine and society.

https://mbsrtraining.com/jon-kabat-zinn/

Randy Taran, made it her mission to help her young son with depression. This was the catalyst for starting the pro-purpose, non-profit, Project Happiness. Her vision in finding resources to help her child soon expanded to the dream of World Happiness Domination.

https://projecthappiness.org/

Megan Tull, certified business and life coach, CEO and founder of Silverlining Concepts, LLC, and author of *The Passion Belief Method: Own Your Value and Earn Your Worth in Business*, Morgan James Publishing, 2016.

https://megantull.com/

Acknowledgments

· · · · · · · · ·

I CHOOSE an attitude of gratitude for all who walked beside me on this journey. **Reggie Adams**, life coach extraordinaire, from deep within my soul I thank you for guiding me toward the light where I could see the writer within and have the courage to bring her home. You nurtured the best in me and invited me to be brave, have an open heart, and move forward. You created a safe space for me and coached me to be curious, creative, and courageous. Thank you for always believing in me. **Julaina Kleist-Corwin**, teacher, coach, and mentor par excellence. Because of your incredible insights and unending patience, I have grown as a writer. Through your classes, workshops, and the community of fellow writers you created, I found a home for my work, my passion, and my voice. I am forever grateful for your kindness and friendship. Editor **Carolyne Ruck**, you handed me the license to speak my truth and find my voice. I thank you for your constant encouragement and cheerleading. **Michelle Radomski**, your unparalleled design work captured the look, feel, and energy I had envisioned for this project. Your passion for perfection combined with patience brought grace and integrity to the process. Writing partner, **Janelle Powers**, thank you for your encouragement, support, intuitive listening skills, and your constant reminders to come from curiosity and care. **Susan Iida-Peterson**, I am grateful for your time and talent. Your insights made this book better. Thank you, editor **Linda Todd**. You took this manuscript to a new level. I appreciate all you did to help me say what I mean with precision and accuracy. To all the attendees of Fuzzy Red Socks Retreats over the years, thank you for allowing me to start you on your self care journeys. And last, but certainly not least, **Rory MacLean**, my husband, my partner, my best friend, and the love of my life. I will be forever grateful to you for standing beside me day after day encouraging me to share my passion for self care with the world. You are the wind beneath my wings.

About the Author

· · · · · · · · ·

Carole MacLean left the corporate world of banking to raise her daughter and open a direct sales business. She moved her aging parents from Ohio to California to help them through cancer, Alzheimer's, and the maze of the medical world. Her support of her parents through the end of their lives, and later her volunteer work as a hospice advocate, led her to write this book. She has been published in local anthologies through the Tri-Valley Writers Club in Pleasanton, California, and is a regular contributor of The Community Book Project with Donna Kozik. Ms. MacLean lives in Scottsdale, Arizona. She volunteers for her local hospice, sings with the West Phoenix Chapter of the Threshold Choir, conducts women's retreats, and blogs about self care at www.fuzzyredsocks.com.